Electronic Keyboard
Grade 6

Pieces & Technical Work
for Trinity College London exam

from 2013

Published by
Trinity College London
Registered office:
89 Albert Embankment
London SE1 7TP UK

T +44 (0)20 7820 6100
F +44 (0)20 7820 6161
E music@trinitycollege.co.uk
www.trinitycollege.co.uk

Registered in the UK
Company no. 02683033
Charity no. 1014792

Pachelbel's Canon

Johann Pachelbel
arr. Victoria Proudler

Voices: Choir (or Pad), Flute, Strings, Trumpet, Violin
Styles: Ballad (bars 1-29) and Dance (bars 30-end)
Split point: Accomp. F#²
Other info: Fingered on bass chord setting to be used in bars 38-54

PLEASE SET UP FOR THE NEXT PIECE

3

1st movement

from Symphony no. 40 in G minor, K. 550

Wolfgang Amadeus Mozart
arr. Andrew Smith

Voices: _____
Style: _____
Other info: Fingered on bass chord setting to be used

* Candidates should refer to the current syllabus requirements for Own Interpretation pieces.

D.S. al Coda

PLEASE SET UP FOR THE NEXT PIECE

Pavane

Gabriel Fauré
arr. Joanna Clarke

Voices:	Flute, Horn, Oboe, Strings
Style:	Hip Hop or Soft Fusion
Split points:	Accomp. A^2 Left Voice G^3
Other info:	Fingered on bass chord setting to be used.
	During dual stave sections, the RH should be played one octave higher than written. All voices to sound at written pitch using octave transpose as necessary.

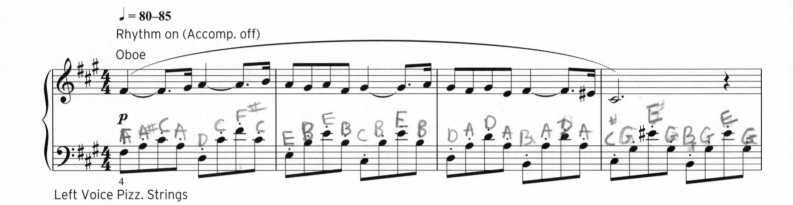

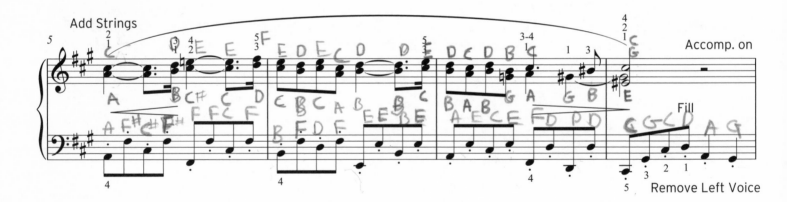

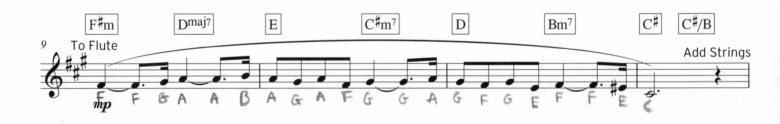

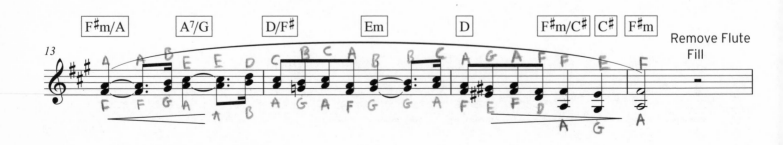

Korobeiniki

(The Pedlars)

Traditional
arr. Andrew Smith

Voices: Lead (Square Lead, Saw Lead), Mandolin, Piano, Strings
Style: Clubdance
Split point: Accomp. G#²

PLEASE SET UP FOR THE NEXT PIECE

Samba Nights

Victoria Proudler

Voices: Brass, Flute, Guitar, Marimba, Piano, Trumpet
Style: Brazilian Samba
Split points: Accomp. bars 1-24 and 57-end F#^{2} Accomp. and Left Voice bars 25-56 C^3
Other info: In bars 25-56, Left Voice chords should be played an octave lower.
               All voices to sound at written pitch using octave transpose as necessary.

PLEASE SET UP FOR THE NEXT PIECE

13

Improvisation

Sir Duke

Words and Music by Stevie Wonder
arr. Joanna Clarke

Voices: Brass, Guitar, Harmonica, Sax.
Style: Funk or Soul
Split point: Accomp. G^2
Other info: Pitch bend to be used where instructed: (↗ = glide upwards
              to written note, ↘ = glide downwards from written note).

The repeat must be
played in the exam.

Technical Work

Candidate should prepare EITHER section i) Scales and Chord Knowledge OR section ii) Exercises. Section i) must be performed from memory; the music may be used for Section ii).

Please see the current syllabus for any further information as requirements can change.

i) Scales and Chord Knowledge

The following scales to be performed in piano voice with auto-accompaniment off, hands together (unless otherwise stated), ♩ = 120, *legato* and mf:

D, F, A♭ and B major (two octaves)

D, F, G♯ and B minor (two octaves): harmonic *and* melodic

Chromatic scales in similar motion starting on *any* black note (two octaves)

Major pentatonic scale starting on D and A♭, straight and swing rhythm, hands separately (two octaves)

Blues scale starting on D and E, straight and swing rhythm, right hand only (two octaves)

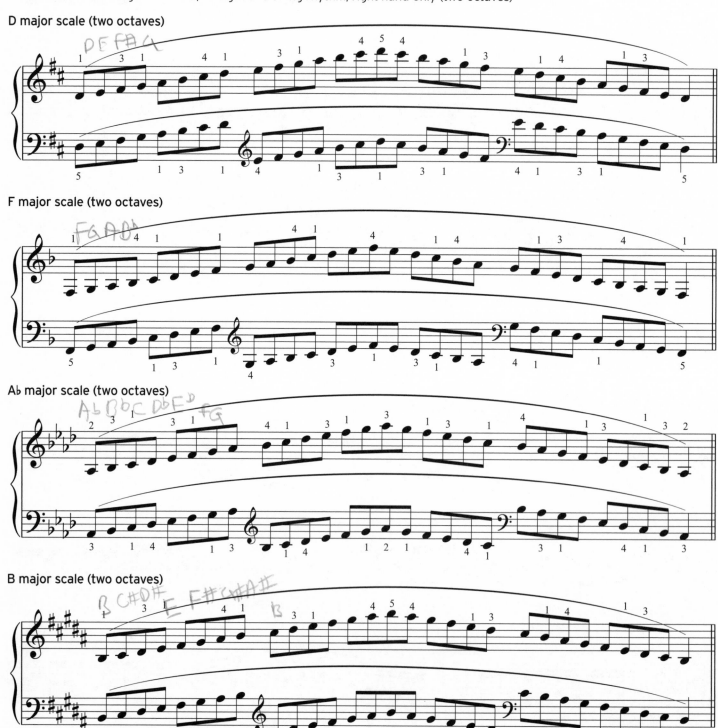

D major scale (two octaves)

F major scale (two octaves)

A♭ major scale (two octaves)

B major scale (two octaves)

D minor scale: harmonic (two octaves)

D minor scale: melodic (two octaves)

F minor scale: harmonic (two octaves)

F minor scale: melodic (two octaves)

G# minor scale: harmonic (two octaves)

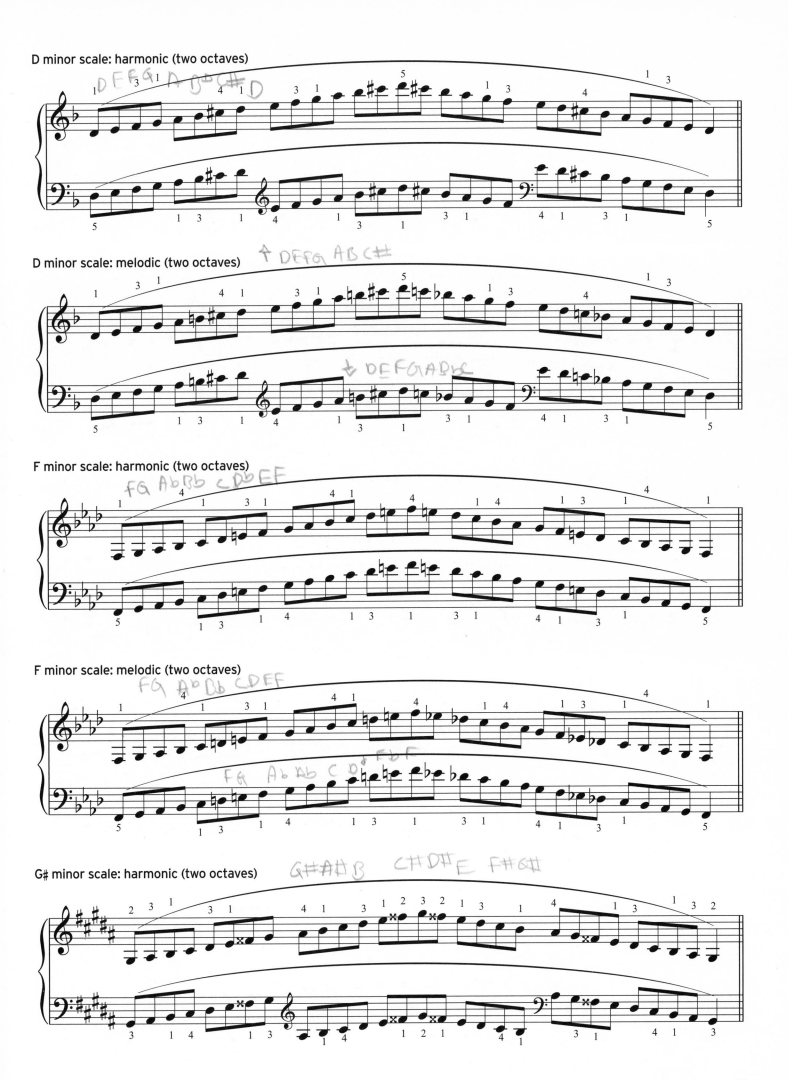

17

G# minor scale: melodic (two octaves)

B minor scale: harmonic (two octaves)

B C# D E F# G A#B

B minor scale: melodic (two octaves)

B C# D E F# G# A#B

B C# D E F# G A B

Chromatic scale in similar motion starting on any black note e.g. Db (two octaves)

18

Major pentatonic scale starting on D (two octaves), straight and swing rhythm

Right hand

Left hand

Major pentatonic scale starting on A♭ (two octaves), straight and swing rhythm

Right hand

Left hand

Blues scale starting on D (two octaves), straight and swing rhythm

Right hand

Blues scale starting on E (two octaves), straight and swing rhythm

Right hand

The following to be performed using piano voice with auto-accompaniment off:

Triad of D, F, A♭ and B major, D, F, G♯ and B minor in all inversions (to be played in the left hand)
Chords of D⁰, F⁰, G♯⁰, B⁰, Dm⁷, Fm⁷, G♯m⁷, Bm⁷, D^{maj7}, F^{maj7}, A♭^{maj7}, B^{maj7} in root position only (to be played with the bass note in the left hand and the chord in the right hand)
Plagal cadence in D and F major

D major

DF♯A

F major

F A C

A♭ major

A♭ C E♭

B major

B D♯ F♯

D minor

D F A

F minor

F A♭ C

G♯ minor

B minor

D° F° G#° B°

Dm⁷ Fm⁷ G#m⁷ Bm⁷

D^maj7 F^maj7 A♭^maj7 B^maj7

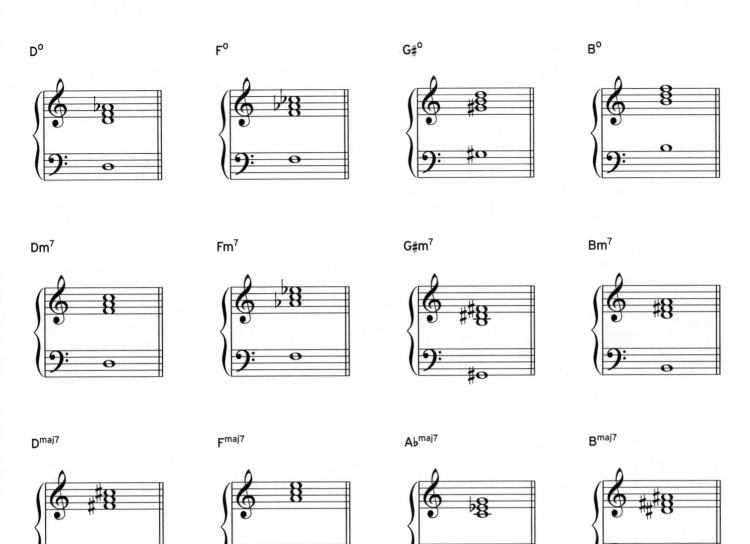

Plagal cadence in D major

Plagal cadence in F major

21

ii) Exercises

Candidate to prepare **all** three exercises; only two exercises will be heard in the exam.

1. Going Round In Circles – for fingered on bass chords and maintaining a relaxed right hand

Voice: Flute
Style: English Waltz
Split point: Accomp. C³
Other info: Fingered on bass chord setting to be used

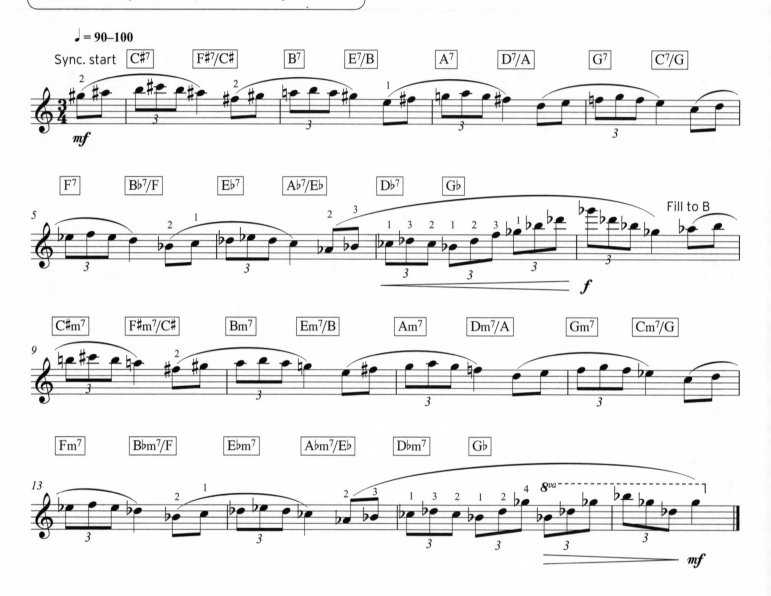

2. Move It! – for left hand dexterity between chords and melody line

Voice:	Piano
Style:	60s Rock
Split point:	Accomp. F#^{2}

* Quavers should be played straight (not swung).

3. Rattletrap – for use of pitch bend

Voice: Synth or Lead
Style: Fusion or Modern R&B or Pop Shuffle
Split point: Accomp. G#^{2}
Other info   Pitch bend range = 2
   ↗ = glide upwards to written note (begin note with wheel in down position and move to midway point).
   ⌃↘ = glide up and down (after note has been played, push wheel from midway point to up position, then back to midway to create a triplet effect).